7
ah, ah,
real - ly have to go. You've been the on - ly thing that's right
Am F Gsus4 G Am F
10
pp
mm.
mp
in all I've done. And I can
Gsus4 G Am F G

13
Ah,
ah,
Ah,
ah,
bare - ly look at you,
but ev - 'ry sin - gle time I do,
Am F Gsus4 G Am F
16
ah.
ah.
I know we'll make it an - y - where a - way from
G Am F Gsus4 G

19
mf f
Oo - ah. Light up, light up, as if you have
mf f
(opening mouth)
Oo - - ah. Oo,
mf f
f
here. Oo - ah. Oo,
Am F G C
mf f
23
a choice. E - ven if you can - not hear my voice,
oo, oo,
oo, oo,
G Am

26
I'll be right be-side you, dear.
mf
mm.
mf
mm.
F6 G/F F Dm/F
29
f
Oo,
oo,
f
Oo,
oo,
f
Loud-er, loud-er, and we'll run for our lives.
C G

32
oo,
oo,
I can hard-ly speak, I un - der-stand, why you can't raise your voice to
Am
35
mp
oo. To think I might not see those eyes,
mp
oo. To think I might not see those eyes,
p
say? Might not see those eyes.
F G/F F Dm/F Am F

38
p
Makes it so hard not to cry. And as we
mf
mp
Makes it so hard not to cry.
So hard not to cry. And as we
Gsus4 G Am F Gsus4 G
41
f
say our long good - byes, I near-ly do.
Long good - byes, I near-ly do.
mf
say our long good - byes, I near-ly do.
Am F Gsus4 G Am F

44
Light up, light up, as if you have
Light up, light up,
f
Ah.
f
Light up, light up, as if you have
G
C
f
47
a choice. E-ven if you can-not hear my voice,
light up. E-ven if you can-not hear my voice,
a choice. E-ven if you can-not hear my voice,
G
Am

50
I'll be right be-side you,_ dear._
Ah.
I'll be right be-side you,_ dear._
Ah._
Mm,
ah._
F
G/F
F
Dm/F
53
ff
Loud-er, loud-er, and we'll run_ for_ our lives.
ff
Loud-er, loud-er, and we'll run for_ our lives.
ff
Loud-er, loud-er, and we'll run for_ our lives.
C
G
ff